MY FIRST EMOJIS™

HOW'S EMOJI?

Melissa Kay Moore

ISBN: 978-0-9989349-2-1 (Paperback)
ISBN: 978-0-9989349-3-8 (Hardcover)

First Edition Book, October 2020

Book cover design, illustration, editing, and interior layout by: 1000 Storybooks

www.1000storybooks.com

Adventures Publishing

DEDICATION

This book is dedicated to all my loving family for supporting and inspiring my dream of writing children's books. Special thanks to my Mom, Sandra, who is my editor extraordinaire. Also to my creative daughters, who always give great advice.

INSIDE OUR HEAD,
A CERTAIN PART OF
THE BRAIN CONTROLS
OUR EMOTIONS.

FOR ALL THESE
EMOTIONS, THERE ARE
EMOJIS!

THINKING MOJI, THINKS...

HMMMM...

HOW'S EMOJI?

WILL YOU HELP MOJI FIND OUT?

GREAT, LET'S GO!

IS EMOJI GLAD?

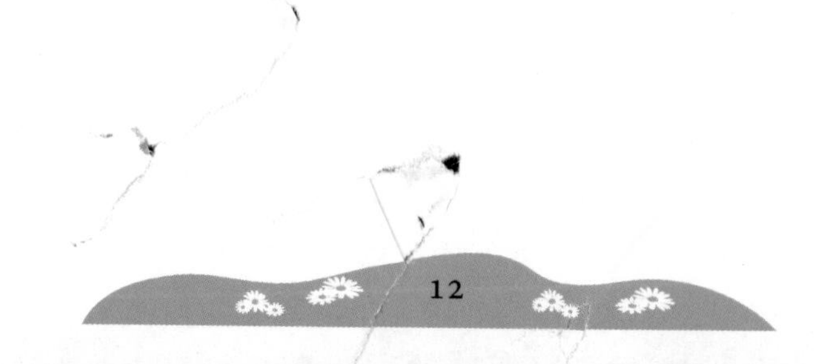

MMM...

IS EMOJI MAD?

GRRR...

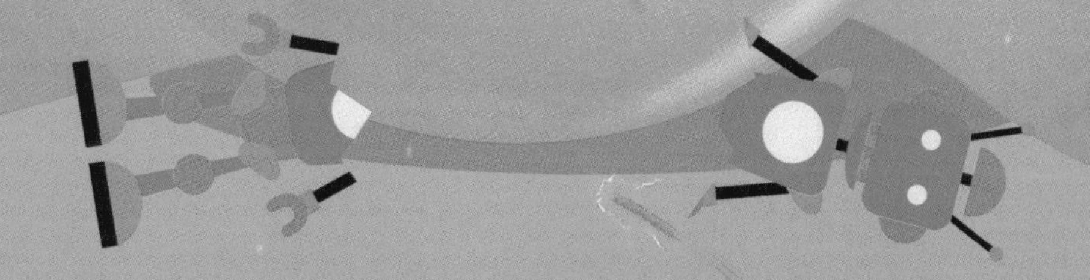

IS EMOJI SAD?

SNIFF...

IS EMOJI SCARED?

GASP!

IS EMOJI TIRED?

YAWN

IS EMOJI EXCITED?

WOW!

NO!

IF EMOJI IS NOT...

THINKING **MOJI**, THINKS...

HMMM...

HOW'S EMOJI?

IS EMOJI HAPPY?

YIPPEE!

IS EMOJI SLEEPY?

ZZZ...

IS EMOJI SILLY?

HEHE...

IS EMOJI DIZZY?

WOAH!

IS EMOJI CRAZY?

WOOHOO!

IS EMOJI ANGRY?

HMPH!

NO!

IF EMOJI IS NOT...

HOW ELSE CAN EMOJI BE?

MOJI LOOKS
AT THE EMOJIPEDIA.

EMOJIPEDIA

MOJI LEARNS THERE ARE
ALL KINDS OF EMOJIS
TO EXPRESS EMOTIONS LIKE...

AND LOTS OF OTHER EMOJIS
TO EXPRESS EMOTIONS TOO!

AFTER SEEING ALL THE EMOJIS MOJI KNOWS HOW IT FEELS TO BE LOVED BY YOU!

AWW...

FROM THE AUTHOR

MELISSA KAY MOORE is excited to share her **MY FIRST EMOJIS**™ educational books to give educators and parents a fun, innovative way to inspire children as early as 2 years old to read. How's Emoji? is the third book, along with What's Emoji? and Where's Emoji?, in the series.

Moore hopes kids will have fun seeing and learning all the fantastic things emojis express, and their use as a universal language in everyday digital communication. She has many more ideas and adventures coming up for Moji in the series, and is enthusiastic for where the journey leads.

Made in the USA
Middletown, DE
03 April 2021